HALTON LEA LIBRARY
Telephone 0151-511-7744

MON	10:00am-5:00pm	THURS	9:00am-7:00pm
TUES	9:00am-7:00pm	FRI	10:00am-5:00pm
WED	10:00am-5:00pm	SAT	10:00am-2:30pm

Bridging the Mersey
a pictorial history

Dave Thompson

European Library ZALTBOMMEL/THE NETHERLANDS

Front cover:

Three of the great bridge spans over the Mersey.

Acknowledgements:

The author wishes to acknowledge his appreciation to the many people and organisations who generously provided photographs or other factual material for use in this book: Jeff Chrimes (Halton Borough Council), Jack Davies (photographer), Ian Douglas, Percy Dunbavand, Halton Localpost UK Ltd, Halton Tourist Information Centre, Denis Hamilton, John Harper, Ron Hignett, Liz Howard, ICI Chlor Chemicals, Institution of Civil Engineers, Bob Martindale, Barry Mawson, Norman Miller, Ray Miller, Charles H. Morris, Raymond Mullin, Derek Seddon, Bert Starkey, Stockport Central Library (Local Studies), Walter Turner, Warrington Library and Widnes & Runcorn Weekly News.

BACK IN TIME

GB ISBN 90 288 2640 8

© 2000 European Library – Zaltbommel/The Netherlands

European Library
post office box 49
NL – 5300 AA Zaltbommel/The Netherlands
telephone: 0031 418 513144
fax: 0031 418 515515
e-mail:publisher@eurobib.nl

Introduction

For thousands of years the River Mersey has been a formidable obstacle to passage. Its name is derived from 'Maeresea' meaning 'boundary river', and it came to form the northern boundary to the ancient Kingdom of Mercia. From Anglo-Saxon times settlements were emerging along the river based on their proximity to narrow crossing points. Ancient fords and ferry services have flourished at various times at Liverpool, Ince, Hale, Runcorn, Fiddlers Ferry, Latchford, Statham near Lymm, Didsbury, Stockport and at other locations up river.

We know that a ford at Latchford offered a lucrative trade to the Boydell family, who had been granted rights to operate a ford or ferry soon after the Norman Conquest. Similar rights were also conferred on the sixth Baron of Halton, John Fitz Richard, who in 1178 had granted a regular charter initiating a ferry at Runcorn. The first fixed bridges were built in the 13th century. In 1285 the Boteler family of Warrington were granted 'pontage' on goods passing over this bridge and its subsequent replacement in 1369. No bridge is thought to have existed in 1453 when the Archbishop of York, together with the Bishops of Durham and Carlisle, called upon Christians to graciously contribute to a new bridge 'over the great and rapid water which was commonly called The Merce, which flows in a swift course to and from the sea, and which, both for inhabitants and strangers who have occasion to travel that way, was troublesome and dangerous to cross'.

The Mersey is formed in Stockport by the confluence of the Goyt and Tame and a bridge here was probably in existence from the same time as that at Warrington. It was sited where the river narrowed to flow through a sandstone ravine. By the 16th century it was called Lancashire Bridge. At one end of the medieval bridge was a chapel known as the 'Hermitage,' where prayers were said for the safety of passengers, who in return offered payment to the priest. A third medieval crossing called the 'Crossford Bridge' is known to have been built near Stretford by the 1530's, all of which must have contributed to the commercial success and growth of all three settlements. Many important historic events have featured the Mersey bridges. During the English Civil War, when Cromwell defeated a Scottish Army at Winwick, he pursued the retreating forces to the Warrington Bridge and rounded-up survivors. The medieval bridges were rebuilt on occasions, most notably in the 18th century after having been broken to delay the forces of Bonnie Prince Charlie from crossing the river at Cheadle Ford and Stockport on their march south.

Over the coming centuries new bridges were added and the railway age brought fresh impetus for new river crossings. Despite some early setbacks the first rail crossing came at Arpley in 1837 and was followed soon after by other schemes. By far the most ambitious of these was a proposal in 1846 by the Grand Junction Railway to construct a line between Runcorn and Ditton in Widnes to shorten the Liverpool-London journey. This scheme was later revived by the London & North Western Railway and provided us with the first of the three great superstructures to span the 1100-ft-wide gap between Runcorn and Widnes. The Ethelfleda Bridge, or Britannia Bridge as it is sometimes known, was one of the first great wrought iron bridges to be borne out of the success of Robert Stephenson's spectacular rail bridge at Menai. It opened in 1868 and still provides a river crossing for west-coast main line trains.

The population of Runcorn and Widnes boomed during the late 19th century, fuelled by the dominance of the chemical industry and the construction of the Manchester Ship Canal along the river shoreline at Runcorn. Many proposals had been prepared for large vehicular crossings of Runcorn Gap but had floundered mainly on cost,

brought about by the technical difficulties of bridging two busy navigable waterways. However, in 1899 the eminent engineer John Webster of Westminster conceived the idea of building the world's largest transporter bridge across the Mersey. The bridge was built at a site that Thomas Telford had himself proposed for a suspension bridge in 1817. For 56 years (between 1905 and 1961) the transporter clattered and banged, to and fro across the Mersey, leaving an indelible mark in the memories of many local people.

From the early 1960's many new bridges have spanned the ever-growing network of towns and cities through which the Mersey passes. The Thelwall Bridge, a viaduct of 4,417 ft in length, was built to carry the M6 motorway over the river and ship canal and at Runcorn Gap, the high-level Road Bridge provided a new vital link across the River Mersey. This huge steel arch crossing gave rise to the growth of Runcorn as a 'New Town' and was the third largest steel-arch structure in the world after Sydney Harbour Bridge and the Bayonne Bridge at New York. It is arguably the most famous structure to cross the Mersey and together with the two previous bridges at Runcorn Gap feature most prominently in this book.

Dave Thompson

1 Long before a bridge crossed the Mersey the only passage to be made was by ferry or ford at low tide. Ancient ferry services operated at various localities along the river. One of the oldest dates from 1178 when Richard Fitz Richard, the sixth Baron of Halton and Constable of Cheshire, granted a charter to the Knight Hospitallers of St. John of Jerusalem. The order was devoted in particular to travellers and pilgrims, some of whom we can assume journeyed to the nearby priory of Augustine canons at Norton. From about 1803 the ferry operated from a landing slip close to the salt-water bathhouse built on the river at Runcorn. Use of the ferry later declined with the opening of the nearby Railway Bridge in 1868 and latterly from the disruption caused by the construction of the Manchester Ship Canal.

Old Ferry and Baths, Runcorn. Photo Chas. A. Timmins, Esq. Copyright.

2   The earliest railway crossing of the River Mersey was opened at Arpley in 1837. It was intended to carry the Grand Junction Railway over both the Mersey and the Runcorn & Latchford Canal and is comprised of a stone viaduct of twelve arches, each differing in proportions. The Mersey and Irwell Navigation Company fought the railway tooth and nail in 1835 over the construction of the viaduct but, when amply compensated for the new restriction on headroom, happily carried all the materials to build the bridge. The magnificent viaduct is still used, although now superseded in use by other railway crossings at Warrington.

3 The magnificent viaduct at Stockport opened in 1839, two years after the Arpley Bridge. It comprised a structure of 26 semi-circular arches, extending over a third of a mile through the town. Eleven million bricks were used in the viaduct, making it the largest brick-built bridge in Britain. Bagshaw's Journal in 1842 described it as 'One of the most daring and stupendous works of art to which the railway has given birth. From the top is experienced one of the most favourable views in England of a manufacturing town'. For more than 120 years it was the highest bridge over the Mersey until the opening in 1961 of the Runcorn-Widnes Bridge. During the golden age of steam it was estimated that five hundred steam engines passed over the Mersey at this point every day.

STOCKPORT VIADUCTS AND RIVER MERSEY.

4 The River Mersey does not entirely follow the line it has always taken, but has been subject to several cuts, damming and diversions, particularly as a means of making the river navigable. One place where the river was diverted was at Warburton, where a graceful cast iron toll bridge has stood since 1843. The bend in the river at this point had been bypassed by the Manchester Ship Canal, leaving the toll bridge as a backwater, soon overgrown with vegetation. Today, motorists still pay to cross from Lymm to Cadishead, although it is not obvious that this is actually an old river crossing point except for the stone abutments and iron railings which are still visible close to the toll house.

5 One of Britain's best known waterways crosses the Mersey at Sale. The Barford viaduct carries the Bridgewater Canal and its towpath across the river, and although it is less well known than James Brindley's remarkable Barton viaduct over the Irwell, it is still deserving of a mention. On the Duke's death in 1803 ownership of the viaduct, like everything else, passed to a trust. As this photograph shows the Bridgewater Canal is still a busy waterway for pleasure craft.

6 A recent picture of Cheadle Bridge, one of the main routes into Manchester on the B5095. The ornate sandstone bridge is the boundary between Manchester and Cheadle and dates from 1861. This is the fourth bridge to stand at this site, the first having been destroyed in 1745 in order to repel the advancing rebels during the Jacobite rebellion. It would appear that this was to no avail as the rebels used the nearby ford and are also thought to have made a temporary crossing by filling the river with felled trees. The present bridge is one of the most attractive dressed stone bridges across the Mersey. It has perhaps avoided the modern concrete widening schemes, which have blighted so many bridges, by the construction of the A34 Kingsway extension at East Didsbury. The depth of the water under Cheadle Bridge is, at present, about 3 ft in fair weather. Although in the 18th century the water would have been a little deeper. It is also likely that wheeled traffic used this place as a ford.

7 The Howley Suspension Bridge at Warrington connects Howley with Latchford. It is one of the most attractive and historic small bridges crossing the Mersey. It was originally intended to construct a larger bridge over the river, but with funds lacking, Warrington Council resolved to cross instead with an ornate pedestrian footway as a temporary measure. Luckily the bridge still survives, after nearly ninety years.

8   The first large span crossing of the Mersey came in 1868 when William Baker, chief engineer to the London & North Western Railway, built a lattice girder iron bridge, crossing the narrows of Runcorn Gap. It required three girders, each of 300 ft, which were fabricated on site using 48,115 rivets and placed piecemeal into position. In this early photograph we see the maze of scaffolding erected across the river to support the construction works. During this time the Railway Company provided steamers to tow vessels on the river through the massive scaffold structure.

9   In this photograph from 1866 we see a top sail schooner being built, and another under repair at the Castle Rock ship building yard at Runcorn. These ships were typical of those sailing to Runcorn in the 19th and early 20th centuries. In the background the Runcorn Railway Bridge is still seen to be under construction. The bridge was built to provide headroom of 75 ft for schooners and other river craft.

10 The completed bridge was officially opened on 21st May 1868 when the locomotive engine 'Cheshire', drawing twenty wagons containing five hundred spectators, made the first journey across the bridge. The impressive bridge is known locally as the Ethelfleda Bridge, and further afield as the Britannia Railway Bridge. It still stands today and is the first of the three great bridges to have been built across Runcorn Gap.

RUNCORN BRIDGE.

11   The excavations for the foundations of the railway bridge piers were originally dug inside coffer-dams, and were each 70 by 40 ft, and 35 ft deep in the sandstone beneath the river bed – an undertaking of some magnitude, even with modern engineering techniques. This view looks down on the sandstone pier on the Runcorn bank now standing in the Manchester Ship Canal. It was at this site during the original excavations for the bridge that remains were discovered which are thought to have been associated with the Saxon fort or 'burgh', first founded by Queen Ethelfleda in 915 A.D to revoke Norse and Danish raiders.

12 An impressive viaduct of arches approached the railway bridge. The approach on the steeply rising Runcorn bank were comparatively short with just 33 arches. However, on the Widnes side, pictured right, it required 65 brick arches and two embankments to raise the line along a wide curve from almost river level at Ditton to meet the 75 ft high span over the Mersey.

WEST BANK VIADUCT, WIDNES

13 The great age of steam is celebrated in this view of a steam locomotive crossing the bridge in the 1950's. The West Coast Main Line route was eventually electrified in 1961.

14 In addition to the double rail track the railway bridge also carried a cantilevered footway across the Mersey and Manchester Ship Canal and for the price of one penny pedestrians could walk across.

L. & N. W. R.

NOTICE IS HEREBY GIVEN

THAT ON AND FROM

27th December, 1920,

The Tolls for Persons & Bicycles, etc.,

PASSING OVER THE

RUNCORN FOOT-BRIDGE

WILL BE AS UNDER:—

Single Journey Toll	**1d.**	
Books of 12 tickets for Single Journey Toll ...	**9d.**	
Single Journey Toll for Bicycle or Handcart ...	**2d.**	
Weekly Ticket for Bicycle or Handcart including Passenger's Toll	**1/9**	

"The act of passing through the registering turnstile, or the acceptance of tickets, is to be taken as evidence of an agreement to the effect that the Company will not be liable to the passenger or his or her representative in consequence of any accident, bodily or otherwise, injury, or delay to the person, or loss or damage to his or her property however caused, which might arise whilst the passenger is using the bridge or footpath, or approaches thereto."

Euston Station, London,
December, 1920.

I. T. WILLIAMS,
General Manager.

M'Corquodale & Co., Limited, Printers, London—Works, Newton.—

15 The footway was a troublesome route over the river as it had to be mounted by a flight of steps on the Runcorn side. Other than the cumbersome ferryboat, which necessitated passengers to climb over the wall of the Manchester Ship Canal, it was the only pedestrian route for some time until the opening of the nearby transporter bridge. The heyday of the footway came in 1952 when the transporter was closed for five months. During that time 250,000 people passed through the turnstiles at Runcorn. The footway is seen in this picture shortly before the completion of the road bridge in 1961.

16   Towards the end of the 19th century the demand for a vehicular bridge crossing at Runcorn was growing irresistibly. A more effective and reliable means of crossing the Mersey between Runcorn and Widnes than that offered by the ferry, was urgently required. Many previous proposals had been made for a crossing at this point but had faltered on cost, largely brought about by the technical difficulties of bridging both the Mersey and Manchester Ship Canal. In 1899 several prominent local businessmen formed the Runcorn & Widnes Bridge Company. It consulted with the leading bridge engineer John Webster of Westminster, who immediately recognized the potential of the so-called 'transbordeur' bridge. This design of bridge carried a suspended ferry above the water, at road level, on the underside of a bridge beam which was set clear of the tallest ships. This idea is pictured here in the Transbordeur Bridge recently built at that time in Rouen, France. The Bridge Company in their prospectus referred to the success of this bridge.

38   ROUEN. — Le Pont Transbordeur. — LL.

17 Two similar bridges of this type were also built for industrial use at the soap works of Joseph Crosfield & Son Ltd in Warrington. The first small transporter bridge was built here in 1905 at the cost of just £4,000 and predominantly conveyed lime sludge for reprocessing on a marshy bend in the river, known locally as the 'tongue land'. The second bridge, pictured here, was opened in 1916 and carried railway wagons from sidings adjacent to the London-Scotland railway line. The 187-ft-span is now derelict but awaits restoration by English Heritage. It has the distinction of being one of only seven transporter bridges that now survive anywhere in the world.

18   In this portrait we see Sir John Brunner, Bart M.P, the member of parliament and influential chemical manufacturer, who had first pioneered the idea of building a transporter bridge across the Mersey between Widnes and Run-corn. Sir John was the Chairman of the Widnes & Runcorn Bridge Company and subscribed much of his own money into the share capital of the venture.

19 Construction work on the Widnes / Runcorn Transporter Bridge commenced in December 1901 at a site upriver of the Railway Bridge. In this view, cast iron cylinders are seen being dug into the Mersey foreshore to support the tower foundations. Each 9-ft-diameter cylinder was bolted to the bare rock and filled with concrete.

20 The laying of foundations on the Runcorn side was more complicated, as the cylinders needed to be sunk in the Manchester Ship Canal. The engineers constructed timber-piled staging from the canal bank to the site for the foundations in the canal, where upon a tramway was laid with a 10-ton steam crane.

21 The sinking of the foundation cylinders in the ship canal proved to be one of the most difficult aspects of the bridge's construction. They were sunk into the canal bed with an air lock on top by means of compressed air caissons. Each was like a huge up-turned funnel in which men worked under com-pressed air, excavating downwards through sand and gravel to the bedrock beneath.

22 The 150-ft-high towers were built throughout 1903 by the Arrol Bridge and Roof Company of Glasgow. The company was founded in 1882 and had a renowned reputation for bridge fabrications. They had also built the first large overhead gauntry at Harland & Wolf's shipyard in Belfast and the gigantic wheels at Earl's Court, Blackpool and Vienna. Arrol built bridges all over the world, but most famously on the Cape-to-Cairo Railway where it is said their bridges, if placed end to end, would extend to over two-and-a-half miles in length. The Arrol Bridge & Roof Company were paid £19 for every ton of steelwork they built into the transporters towers and used a 120-ft-high triangular framed scaffold with a 5-ton crane capable of lifting pieces to the highest parts of the towers, where men worked at a pace using pneumatic riveting machines.

23 Ornate copper-topped lanterns, finished with wooden panels and windows, were erected on the top of each tower. Following the bridge's demolition one of these lanterns is reputed to have been used as a sweet shop on the road to Chester.

24   In this view the cables from the St. Helens Cable Company are seen to be arriving at the bridge construction site. The cables were unique and required 5,000 tests on their composition and the breaking load of the wires before the engineers could be satisfied as to their suitability. Each cable comprised 2,413 wires and each wire was designed to withstand a load of 90 tons per square inch.

25 The heavy chemical-laden atmosphere of Widnes was of particular worry to the engineers. The senior engineer, John Webster, was so concerned about the acidity of the atmosphere that he had cables coated with a bitumen compound and wrapped with sailcloth also saturated in bitumen. He had determined the resistance of the bitumen to the poisonous atmosphere by having tested this and other substances on coated wrought-iron plates and for three months had them suspended 50 ft above a Widnes chemical works.

Widnes

26   In this view we see one of the huge saddles used for carrying the cables over the top of the towers. These were designed to allow for the varying expansion and contraction of the cables, brought about by the differing loads and temperatures experienced.

27 A rare view of workmen, employed in the construction of the bridge, together with their families during a trip to celebrate the completion of the transporter bridge. This gathering in 1905 is believed to have been taken at Frodsham.

28 The new transporter bridge seen from Victoria Gardens, Widnes.
This viewpoint of the two Mersey crossings was described by the writer of this postcard as 'the only decent place that I have seen around this peculiar town'. This attractive promenade area was developed in 1884 and after the construction of the transporter it became a popular resting place with bridge passengers and local folk.

THE GREAT SPAN OVER THE MERSEY, 1000 FEET. LINKING, LANCASHIRE TO CHESHIRE. OPENED, 29/5/05.

29   John James Webster (1845-1914), the Warrington-born engineer responsible for the construction of two famous bridges across the Mersey, the Widnes Transporter Bridge and Warrington Bridge at Bridge Foot. The eminent Westminster-based engineer had a worldwide reputation for bridge and pier building, before he embarked on the design of Britain's first transporter bridge early in 1900. He went on to build the Shepherds Bush Stadium for the 1908 Olympic games before Warrington Corporation commissioned him in 1912 to oversee the new crossing at Bridge Foot, Warrington. Webster's scheme for Bridge Foot was to result in one of the earliest examples of a reinforced concrete bridge and at 80 ft in width, the second widest bridge in the country after Westminster Bridge in London.

30   Since the 13th century seven bridges are known to have been built across the river at 'Bridge Foot' in Warrington, making it the most frequently bridged location on the Mersey. For centuries these structures formed the only regular bridging of the river for travellers in south-west Lancashire and north Cheshire. In this postcard view looking towards Bishops Wharf we see the fifth bridge, opened in 1837, during the first years of Queen Victoria's reign. The bridge survived until the first half of its replacement bridge was partially opened in 1913.

31 The sixth bridge, pictured here in 1928, is that built by John Webster. It spanned 134 ft across the river and is 80 ft between parapets and contains 2,400 cubic yards of concrete and 242 tons of steel. The new Warrington Bridge was opened in two halves, the earlier opening in 1913 having been performed by King George V, and the second half in 1915. It is still in use today, although now providing a one-way interchange of five lanes.

New Bridge, Warrington.

32 A second major road crossing of the Mersey at Warrington was provided when the 'Kingsway Bridge' was opened by Alderman David Tinnion in 1934. It originally helped divert traffic away from the town centre and provided a more direct means of access for those frustrated from having to journey to Bridge Foot. The A50 crosses the bridge and it still provides one of the main thoroughfares across Warrington. The ferro-concrete structure has two arches of 86 ft and an overall span of 180 ft with 60 ft between the parapets.

33 The official opening of Webster's transporter bridge at Widnes took place on 29th May 1905. During the ceremony Alderman Quinn, the Mayor of Widnes, received three hundred guests at the Town Hall in Victoria Square before a procession moved to the approaches of the bridge where John Webster greeted them. In this picture we see the procession as it nears the transporter from Mersey Road, Widnes.

34 Sir John Brunner, Bart M.P, performed the opening ceremony. Afterwards he crossed to Runcorn in his own motor car, accompanied by other prominent figures in the Widnes & Runcorn Bridge Company.

35 One of the last ferry-boats which, for 690 years, was the sole means of crossing the Mersey at this point. The boatman in this picture is Mr. Harrison, the last ferryman. The ancient ferry service, made famous in Stanley Holloway's ballad 'Tuppence per Person per Trip', first began from Runcorn in 1178. It was discontinued with the opening of the transporter bridge in 1905.

36　No mains electricity was available in the vicinity of the transporter bridge and a generating station to supply power for the motors was built within the base of the Widnes east tower. The interior of the three-storey building can be seen in this rare view of the power house. It contained a pair of 75-brake horsepower Crossley gas engines, installed by Messrs Mather & Platt, the renowned electrical engineers who had previously supplied electrical plant for powering the tramways at Blackpool, Fleetwood and the Isle of Man. The gas supply for the power house came from the Widnes mains supply. The Engineering magazine records, 'As the price of gas is no more than 1 s. per 1000 cu ft, it will be seen that the running costs are every low, and it is estimated that the power for each trip of the transporter is supplied for 1d'.

37 In this scene we see the transporter car and its passengers on their journey across the river. When working in parallel, with a load of about 10 tons and favourable weather conditions, the car was capable of crossing in one-and-a-half minute but normally journey time varied between three and four minutes. The ornate car could carry three hundred passengers and four 2-horse wagons. Shelter accommodation was provided for passengers to help protect them from the elements. The driver controlled the car from his cabin, seen pictured here over the top of the platform.

ELECTRIC CAR, CROSSING SHIP CANAL TO WIDNES.

38　Despite optimistic forecasts the transporter bridge made a substantial loss in its early years. Sir John Brunner thought the bridge to be of no commercial concern, and offered to transfer his share holdings to both local authorities. Runcorn Urban District Council declined to purchase, but the Borough of Widnes accepted, resulting in the complete transfer of ownership to the Corporation in 1911. Widnes Corporation undertook substantial refurbishment of the transporter, which included the replacement of the electric drive propulsion with a new haulage system of cable winches. In this postcard from 1913 we see the reopening ceremony performed again by Sir John Brunner at the invitation of Widnes Corporation.

SIR J. T. BRUNNER, REOPENS THE WIDNES TRANSPORTER BRIDGE. 21/11/13.

39   From his cabin the driver of the transporter had an uninterrupted view in all directions, allowing him to ensure that no disruption occurred to shipping on the river and Manchester Ship Canal. However, in one incident during 1914 the car collided with the river flat 'Annie Abel'. It resulted in legal proceedings being brought against the Corporation of Widnes, but fortunately there were no injuries. The transporter car seen in this photograph is the second carriage built during the first major refurbishment of the bridge in 1913.

40 A rare aerial view of
Runcorn Gap, showing the
transporter bridge and the
railway bridge.

THE TRANSPORTER AND RUNCORN BRIDGES.   WIDNES.

41 The strategic significance of the transporter bridge meant that it attracted many celebrity passengers journeying to Liverpool, Lancashire and Cheshire. In 1913 King George V travelled over the bridge and was so intrigued by the interior of the driver's cabin that he kept his party waiting. Eventually Lord Derby, who was accompanying the King, reminded him that they were behind schedule with the day's itinerary. The King still had much to learn about the workings of the carriage and took his time, apparently being fascinated by the cabin's similarity to a ship's cabin. He returned to Widnes in 1925 and, as can be seen in this picture postcard, made a second visit to the driver's cabin.

42 Royal visits have always been regarded by locals as a special occasion and crowds gathered whenever members of the royal family crossed the river. This crowd has gathered in 1958 to welcome the Queen Mother. During her visit to Widnes she spent time inspecting models and plans of the new road bridge which was then already under construction and was later to climb the transporter bridge's tower to view progress. However, due to windy weather the Queen Mother never climbed the bridge and as a consequence arrived ahead of schedule at Runcorn. It is a matter of some amusement that the unsuspecting dignitaries expecting to welcome the Queen Mother to Runcorn had sheltered from the weather in a nearby pub. Unaware that their royal guest was ahead of schedule they emerged to stampede down to Waterloo Road, with top hats flying hither and thither as the Queen Mother's carriage came into 'dock'.

43 A charabanc outing of Conservative ladies is pictured here on the Widnes approach to the transporter in 1920. The increasing amount of road traffic at this time led to speed restrictions being imposed on the approach roads to the bridge. In 1920 Runcorn Urban District Council wrote to all headmasters in Runcorn asking them to 'warn their scholars against the dangerous practice of following charabancs coming from the transporter bridge'.

44 In this picture from the late 1950's vehicles are seen boarding the transporter car.

45 A Time Table for the transporter bridge published by the Widnes Corporation in 1957. The service, when working, generally operated during its 56-year history at 20-minute intervals, thus allowing 10 minutes for the car to cross and discharge its load before taking on a new one. In 1907 the corporation had introduced an experimental bus service to meet with the car docking on the Widnes approach. This service originally used four covered-top double deck omnibuses and was made a permanent service in 1909. It has the unique distinction of being the world's first double-decker bus service.

TIME TABLE

WEEK DAYS

Car Leaves WIDNES.			Car Leaves RUNCORN		
a.m.	noon	p.m.	a.m.	p.m.	p.m.
5.25	12.0A	6.10	5.30	12.5	5.45B
5.40	p.m.	6.30	5.45	12.20	6.0
5.50	12.10	6.50	6.0	12.40	6.20
6.10	12.30	7.10	6.20	12.50	6.40
6.30	12.45	7.30	6.40	1.0	7.0
6.45	12.55	7.50	6.50	1.20	7.20
6.55	1.10	8.10	7.0	1.40	7.40
7.10	1.30	8.30	7.15	2.0	8.0
7.30	1.50	8.50	7.40	2.20	8.20
7.50	2.10	9.10	8.0	2.40	8.40
8.10	2.30	9.30	8.15	3.0	9.0
8.20	2.50	9.50	8.25	3.20	9.20
8.30	3.10	10.10	8.40	3.40	9.40
8.50	3.30	10.30	9.0	4.0	10.0
9.5	3.50	10.50	9.10	4.20	10.20
9.15	4.10	11.10	9.20	4.40	10.40
9.30	4.30	11.30	9.40	4.55B	11.0
9.50	4.50		10.0	5.0A	11.20
10.10	5.0B		10.20	5.5B	11.35
10.30	5.10		10.40	5.15B	
10.50	5.20B		11.0	5.20A	
11.10	5.30		11.20	5.25B	
11.30	5.40B		11.40	5.35B	
11.50	5.50A		11.55A	5.40A	

A—Saturdays Only.　　B—Saturdays Excepted.

SUNDAYS

Car Leaves Widnes	Car Leaves RUNCORN
9 a.m. and 9-10 a.m., and every 20 minutes until 11.30 p.m.	9.5 a.m. and 9.20 a.m. and every 20 minutes until 11.35 p.m.

This Time Table will be adhered to as far as possible, but the Corporation accept no responsibility for any errors, discrepancies, stoppages or delays.

S. CROSSLEY, *Manager*.

BOROUGH OF WIDNES

WIDNES

Transporter Bridge

Telephone : No. 2746 Widnes

Time Table

And List of

TOLLS AND CHARGES

December, 1957, and until further notice

Swale (Widnes) Limited.

46 In 1957 the trip across the river cost 2d. per person per trip but at 4d wasn't so cheap if you transported your sheep or pigs. There were 31 separate toll charges for passengers, animals and different forms of transport. The tolls shown on this page make interesting reading, but fortunately were not as complex as those shown in the original enabling Act in 1900. In those days there were 112 separate toll charges, not only for fare-paying passengers but also for cockles, vinegar, nails, oranges, pianos and a host of other commodities. In fact it cost five times as much to journey across if you happened to be dead at the time: a standard adult corpse without bearers at five old pence!

WIDNES CORPORATION TRANSPORTER BRIDGE.

LIST OF TOLLS AND CHARGES

		s.	d.
MOTOR VEHICLES.			
Motor-Car		1	0
or if carrying Goods, Advertising Matter, Samples, etc.		1	6
COMMERCIAL VEHICLES, CARAVANS, VANS, MOTOR COACHES, BRAKES, ESTATE CARS, ETC.			
For each vehicle—			
Not exceeding 15 cwt. tare (empty) ...		1	0
or which together with load does not exceed 1 ton 10 cwt. (gross)		1	6
Exceeding 15 cwt. but not exceeding 1 ton 5 cwt. tare (empty)		1	3
or which together with load does not exceed 2 tons 10 cwt. (gross)		2	3
Exceeding 1 ton 5 cwt. but not exceeding 2 tons 10 cwt. tare (empty)		2	0
or which together with load does not exceed 5 tons (gross)		3	9
Exceeding 2 tons 10 cwt. but not exceeding 5 tons tare (empty)		3	9
or which together with load does not exceed 10 tons (gross)		7	6
Exceeding 5 tons but not exceeding 6 tons tare (empty)		4	6
or which together with load does not exceed 10 tons (gross)		7	6
ADDITIONAL CHARGES.			
For each ton or part of a ton in excess of the before-mentioned gross weights			9
Exceeding 6 tons but not exceeding 10 tons tare (no trailers allowed) per ton or part of a ton (empty)			9
or which together with load does not exceed 10 tons		7	6
Trailers drawn by Motor Vehicles (restricted to trailer not exceeding 3 tons when empty nor 5 tons when loaded) :—			
The like tolls as these charged for Motor Vehicles pursuant to the foregoing scale.			

Drivers of Motor Vehicles will be required to produce a Consignment Note showing the correct nett weight carried at the time of crossing, on the request of any Officer of the Bridge.

The maximum Gross Weight allowed for any vehicle shall be 10 tons (inclusive).

WIDNES CORPORATION TRANSPORTER BRIDGE.

LIST OF TOLLS AND CHARGES

		s.	d.
HORSE VEHICLES.			
Cab, Shandry, Gig, or other light vehicle ...		1	0
Cart, Lorry, or Float, which together with its load (if any) does not exceed 1 ton ...		1	0
Every additional part of a ton up to 10 cwt.			6
Each animal beyond the first attached to any vehicle			6
PASSENGERS.			
Adults (children in arms only free) ...			2
Children under 14 years of age			1
CYCLES.			
One person included			4
MOTOR CYCLES.			
(Driver free)			6
With Side-Car (including/or three-wheeler)			9
OTHER CHARGES.			
Perambulators and Baby Carriages			3
Small Truck, Wheelbarrow, Handcart or other small vehicle, loaded or empty			6
Large Handcart, Handbarrow, etc.			9
Horse, Mule, Ass, or Head of Cattle,			
Calf, Pig, Sheep (on foot)			4
Corpse, Adult (with six bearers)		5	3
Corpse, Child (with four bearers)		3	0
Motor Hearse		2	3

In regard to any other article or thing, such reasonable toll and charge as the Corporation may think fit to impose

A passenger may take luggage not exceeding 28 lb. free.

All previous Lists of Tolls and Charges are hereby cancelled.

By Order,

S. CROSSLEY,

Manager.

47 One of the tickets is-
sued to passengers for
crossing the Mersey on the
Widnes Transporter Bridge.

48 Scenes of celebration in West Bank, Widnes, are seen here during the 1951 Festival of Widnes. This formed part of the nation-wide Festival of Britain celebrations and Widnes Corporation decided to have the transporter bridge specially floodlit for the occasion.

49　The famous Mersey bridges have served as a backdrop for many family occasions and are undoubtedly the most photographed features on the river together with the Liverpool waterfront. Children in particular saw the transporter as something of an adventure. The slow speed, movement of the spring-loaded car and the clanking of the machinery were something akin to a cross between being on the deck of a ship, footplate of a railway engine and in the gondola of an airship. Children would use the carriage as a pulley, and hang beneath the car as it crossed the river. On the Widnes foreshore many children would shout to passengers in the car to throw pennies for them to collect.

50 The transporter resembled a giant Meccano model and the Liverpool-based company even produced a pre-assembly kit of the bridge for consumers. This particular working model, pictured here, was displayed at the world's largest Meccano exhibition in Henley-on-Thames. The 16-ft structure was made by Nick Rodgers from Surrey and incorporated 4,000 nuts and bolts, considerably less than its full-size namesake. It is also believed that during one of Lord Haw's wartime broadcasts he is reputed to have commented: 'And we have not forgotten Widnes and its Meccano Bridge.'

Regardless of his taunts it had naturally been expected that the Mersey bridges would be a target for the Luftwaffe but no attack ever came, despite the proximity of the chemical works and their strategic importance for Liverpool.

51 The transporter made its last journey for fare-paying passengers at 6 p.m. on the opening day of the new road bridge. The following morning, on 22nd July 1961, crowds gathered around the Widnes approach of the transporter bridge to witness the last ever journey to Runcorn, led by the Mayor of Widnes, Councillor John Collins, and Chairman of the Corporation's Transport Committee, Alderman Pat Hanley. Amongst the specially invited guests provided with the souvenir tickets to attend were former drivers and others employed or associated with the bridge over the years.

1905   1961

Widnes Transporter Bridge

Official Closing Ceremony
Saturday, 22nd July, 1961

SOUVENIR TICKET FOR THE
LAST TRIP

Name of Passenger   J. White, Esq.

52 The Mayor of Widnes, Councillor John Collins, is seen joined with other dignitaries as the transporter car slips away from Widnes on its last journey to Runcorn. Flags were hoisted, the band sounded a fanfare and maroons flared as the transporter made its way amidst much waving and cheering.

53 A huge crowd awaited the car's arrival in Runcorn and gave it a great welcome as it rattled in for the last time. Here another fifty guests embarked, led by Councillor Murial Preece, Chairman of the Runcorn Urban District Council. At seven minutes past eleven the transporter's own hooter signalled the very last departure and there arose a chorus of sirens from the tugboats on the ship canal. The bells of Runcorn Parish Church rang out and then, accompanied by the crowd, all joined in singing 'Now is the hour for us to say goodbye'. The car moved off to Widnes on its last journey to accompaniment from ships' sirens. The Runcorn Weekly News records: 'This was the most nostalgic moment of all for the passengers as they watched the Widnes shore drawing near. People waiting on the Widnes side now joined in the singing.' The car is seen in this view soon after it came to rest at the Widnes approach.

54 A unique meeting occurred at the closing ceremony of the transporter bridge. On the left is 84-year-old Mr. Shaw, the first driver of the transporter during its opening in 1905, and right Mr. Done, the last driver of the car during the closing ceremony.

55 A small ceremonial presentation was made at the Widnes approach after the last journey had been made across the river. Mr. Crossley, the General Manager of the bridge, is seen here presenting to the Mayor the driver's handle as a souvenir for the people of Widnes. The chrome-plated handle is still preserved and is displayed in the Mayor's Parlour at Runcorn Town Hall. It has become a talking point at many mayoral functions down the years, and is often shown to visiting dignitaries.

56 In this picture Pat Hanley, Chairman of the Widnes Corporation's Transport Committee, unveils a bronze plaque to commemorate the passing of the transporter bridge. It records 'The transporter bridge owned by the Corporation since 1911, carried over a million foot passengers and over a quarter of a million vehicles between this spot and Runcorn each year'. The plaque and two other commemorative plaques from the bridge were mounted on the Widnes approach after the bridge had been demolished at a cost of £139,604. Other than the small sandstone power-house on the Widnes approach, little more reminds us of the great transporter that once spanned the Mersey at this site.

57 The impact of the transporter's closure on the commercial life of West Bank in Widnes was immediate and quite severe. Down the years many shops had emerged along Mersey Road to service the needs of passengers, many of whom shopped whilst waiting to cross the river. The Road Bridge's high level approaches bypassed West Bank altogether, resulting in the closure of many shops. This picture shows the quiet scene at Widnes approach, days after it had thronged with travellers.

58   Demand for a new vehicular road bridge to replace the transporter bridge between Runcorn and Widnes reached a peak in the 1940's. It resulted in the Runcorn-Widnes Bridge Act 1946, which empowered a new crossing of Runcorn Gap. From 1946 to 1957 four different schemes were considered and rejected, either on the grounds of cost or from problems associated with the results of aerodynamic tests. Early proposals for a suspension bridge had been abandoned when it became evident that the proposed bridge would oscillate severely, owing to the bluff shape of the near-by railway bridge. Finally the steel arch structure, picture right, was agreed and work commenced in 1956.

59 The high-level 1,628-ft-long steel arch bridge was designed to stand 75 ft above the river level and provide a clear headroom of 80 ft for shipping on the Manchester Ship Canal. A bridge of this scale necessitated the demolition of housing either side of the river to help make way for almost three-quarters of a mile of viaducts. Many old Victorian terraced streets disappeared altogether. Pictured here is the demolition of Viaduct Street and Irwell Street in Widnes.

60 The Widnes approach road seen under construction in September 1959. The building to the right is West Bank Primary School.

61 The design of the bridge's foundations were an important aspect of construction. The foundations of the footings on the Widnes side were buried into the Mersey foreshore and at Runcorn, on the bank of the Manchester Ship Canal. The two concrete foundations were designed to withstand 2,950 tones of thrust from each bridge truss. The boatyard seen to the left in this view is that of Richard Abel & Sons. It had originally occupied the site of the foundations but the boatyard later moved nearer the transporter bridge to make way for the bridge's construction. Abel's were renowned builders of schooners and barges, until 1953, when they concentrated their business solely on boat repairs.

62 The erection of the
Widnes span is underway
in July 1959.

63   By June 1960 the spans from either side of the river were moving closer together. Pictured in this view we see the 20-ton creeper cranes which moved slowly up the structure, where workmen then riveted steelwork into place. The Runcorn-Widnes Bridge has the distinction of being the last major bridge that used rivets in its construction.

64 A view of the three great Mersey crossings between Runcorn and Widnes, pictured shortly before the completion of the Runcorn-Widnes Bridge. Both creeper cranes can be seen to have almost completed construction of the whole arch. Afterwards they were slowly reversed down the arch halves, erecting the steelwork on the deck and hangers as they went. The creeper cranes were made from steelwork that could later be used in the final completion of the bridge. This picture was taken from the Old Quay locks that join the Manchester Ship Canal with the River Mersey at Runcorn. These locks were built to allow river traffic to pass into the ship canal. They closed in the 1970's.

65 In this unique view the two halves of the span are finally brought together, leaving a gap of about 20 inches. This was closed by letting the remaining cables out gradually until the two halves met. This method of gradually letting down the immensely heavy bridge halves is a process known as fleeting. Engineers had to plan when this was undertaken as the gap would continue to open and close due to the natural temperature changes in the 5,900 tons of steelwork.

66 For a short period of time all three of the great bridges across Runcorn Gap were present side by side. Soon after they had completed work on the construction of the Road Bridge, workers from the Dorman Long (Bridge & Engineering) Company demolished the transporter bridge.

67 The Runcorn-Widnes Road Bridge was officially opened by H.R.H. Princess Alexandra of Kent on 21st July 1961. At that time it was the third longest steel arch bridge in the world, only surpassed in size by the Sydney Harbour Bridge (1,650 ft) and Bayonne Bridge (1,652 ft) at New York. Several other larger, steel arch superstructures were built in the years immediately after it opened and Runcorn-Widnes Bridge is now the ninth longest in the world. In engineering terms the bridge heralded a new era of large span British bridges. The Severn Suspension Bridge and Forth Road Bridge were both underway by the time of Runcorn-Widnes Bridge's opening. (Photo: Weekly News.)

68 The bunting still flies in this 1961 view of trouble-free motoring over the new Runcorn-Widnes Bridge. However, the ease by which traffic could cross the river would soon change and by 1970 slow moving traffic was a common sight. Momentum grew for action to be taken to relieve congestion, resulting in 1972 in new proposals to widen the bridge to four lanes.

69 The famous Mersey bridges are one of the best known landmarks in the north-west and have featured in many souvenirs such as these commemorative stamps by Halton Localpost UK. This independent postal service was first established in 1986 and has used the images of the bridges in many special souvenir stamps. Those pictured here were produced for Age Concern and to celebrate the 1987 Halton Show. They can be used in place of stamps produced by the royal mail and have taken the image of the Mersey crossings through letter boxes all over the world.

70 A jubilant handshake between William Rodgers M.P, Secretary of State for Transport, and Councillor George Ford at the opening of the bridge widening scheme in October 1977. The £12 million improvements included the conversion of the bridge to accommodate two additional lanes of traffic, construction of a new cantilevered walkway and several kilometres of dual carriageway on the approaches to the bridge. The work had taken over two years and during that time the bridge was only completely closed for one day. During the widening programme it was announced that the bridge would be renamed the 'Silver Jubilee Bridge', to commemorate the completion of the works during the Queen's silver jubilee.

71 Children crossing to Widnes on the cantilevered walkway of the Silver Jubilee Bridge.

72   Despite its widening in 1977 traffic congestion continued to be a major source of anxiety for motorists. Today 80,000 vehicles a day cross the bridge, making it during rush hour one of the most renowned bottlenecks in the north-west. Experts predict that by 2025 this figure will have increased to 125,000 vehicles a day. This has led to fresh claims for a new, second road crossing over the River Mersey between Runcorn and Widnes. (Photo: Weekly News.)

73 The upkeep and main-
tenance of the Silver Jubilee Bridge costs £1 million
a year and includes regular
painting, resurfacing and
concrete repairs to bridge
supports. In this picture
from the early 1980's we
see the bridge being closed
for repair work.

74 The lights which illuminate the Silver Jubilee Bridge were first switched on to coincide with the BBC's 'Children in Need' celebrations in November 1994. They comprise 164 lamps fitted on purpose-made brackets attached to the bridge parapets. The bridge is one of the largest illuminated structures in Britain.

75 The Silver Jubilee Bridge is the scene of one of the most astonishing migrations of birds anywhere in the country. During the winter months it is estimated that up to one million starlings settle on the bridge to roost. Over the years many different methods have been used to discourage the feathered fiends, including the use of amplified distress calls, pyrotechnics, strobe lighting and loud explosives. Other suggestions considered have included applying non-setting gel on the ledges used by the birds, spikes attached to the steelwork, plastic hawks and twine, which produces a humming sound in the wind. Despite the costly array of gadgets and proposals nothing has prevented the nightly scene of birds on the bridge. (Photo: Weekly News.)

76 In April 2000 hundreds of people made history by becoming the first to run over the Silver Jubilee Bridge. The Halton Road Race 2000 was organized by Halton Borough Council as part of their Millennium celebrations. It was the first time in the 40-year history of the bridge that it had been given over to pedestrian use. Race Director Jim Ross told the Runcorn World: 'The runners were made up the bridge had been given over to them and not the starlings.'